NOLAN'S ARK

and a day at the park

Written by Jordan Hennessey Illustrated by Emma Winterbottom

Nolan's Ark and a day at the park
Written by Jordan Hennessey
Illustrated by Emma Winterbottom

Illustrations by Emma Winterbottom
Publishing support by fleck creative studio

Printed in Canada

ISBN 978-1-7778150-1-1

This book is
dedicated to
Nolan and Brooks,
and in loving memory
of Sophia

This book belongs to

____

A is for Alligators
splashing all about ☺

B is for Bears
fishing for some trout ☺

HAP
BIRTH

C is for Caterpillar
slithering on the ground☺

D is for Dalmatians
heading homeward bound☺

E is for Eagle
soaring through the skies ☺

F is for Fox
with the mischievous eyes ☺

G is for Gazelle
the desert king☺

H is for Hermit Crab
hear him sing☺

I is for Iguana
eating all the bugs 🙂

J is for Jellyfish
don't give it HUGS! 🙂

WAVES
ARE
COOL

K is for Kangaroo
and her little pouch 🙂

L is for Lion
lazy on a couch 🙂

Z Z z z

M is for Moose fierce and wise

N is for Night Hawk AND a falcon, oh what a surprise!

O is for Octopus
with many many arms

P is for Piggies
oink oink oink on the farm

abc

Oink!
Oink!

Q is for Quagga
half zebra half horse ☺

R is for Rabbit
delivering chocolate of
course ☺

S is for Sea Cucumber but be sure not to eat it ☺

T is for Tasmanian Devil nice in person when you meet it ☺

Nice to meet you!

U is for Unicorn
with an ice cream brain
freeze 🙂

V is for Vulture
staring down from the trees 🙂

W is for Whale
swimming in an ocean so
blue

X is for Xenosaurus
a lizard, who knew?

Y is for Yak
from the mountain ☺

Z is for Zonkey
drinking from a fountain! ☺

Jordan is originally from Victoria, BC and his nephews keep him young.

Emma is an artist and illustrator from Vancouver, BC and this is her first children's book.

Made in the USA
Monee, IL
20 March 2022